Calvin and Hobbes
by Bill Watterson

Andrews McMeel Publishing, LLC

Kansas City • Sydney • London

Andrews McMeel Publishing, LLC
an Andrews McMeel Universal company
1130 Walnut Street, Kansas City, Missouri 64106

ISBN: 978-1-4494-0709-4

www.andrewsmcmeel.com

To Our Beloved Mia, The older you get, the brighter you shine!! Happy Birthday! Mom + Dad

---

ATTENTION: SCHOOLS AND BUSINESSES

Andrews McMeel books are available at quantity discounts with bulk purchase for educational, business, or sales promotional use. For information, please e-mail the Andrews McMeel Publishing Special Sales Department: specialsales@amuniversal.com.

Foreword

There are few wellsprings of humor more consistently reliable than the mind of a child. Most cartoonists, being childlike, recognize this, but when they set out to capture the hurly-burly of the very young, they almost always cheat, shamelessly creating not recognizable children, but highly annoying, wisecracking, miniature adults. Chalk it up to either indolence or defective recall, but most people who write comic dialogue for minors (up to and including the perpetrators of the Cosby "kids") demonstrate surprisingly little feel for—or faith in—the original source material, that is, childhood, in all its unfettered and winsome glory.

It is in this respect that Bill Watterson has proved as unusual as his feckless creations, Calvin and Hobbes. Watterson is the reporter who's gotten it right; childhood as it actually *is*, with its constantly shifting frames of reference. Anyone who's done time with a small child knows that reality can be highly situational. The utterance which an adult knows to be a "lie" may well reflect a child's deepest conviction, at least at the moment it pops out. Fantasy is so accessible, and it is joined with such force and frequency, that resentful parents like Calvin's assume they are being manipulated, when the truth is far more frightening: they don't even exist. The child is both king and keeper of this realm, and he can be very choosey about the company he keeps.

Of course, this exclusivity only provokes many grown-ups into trying to regain the serendipity of youth for themselves, to, in effect, retrieve the irretrievable. A desperate few do things that later land them in the Betty Ford Center.

The rest of us, more sensibly, read Calvin and Hobbes.

— GARRY TRUDEAU

TO
MELISSA

OUTRAGE! WHY SHOULD I GO TO BED? I'M NOT TIRED! IT'S ONLY 7:30! THIS IS TYRANNY! I'M!

8

BAD NEWS, DAD. YOUR POLLS ARE WAY DOWN.

MY POLLS?

YOU RATE ESPECIALLY LOW AMONG TIGERS AND SIX-YEAR-OLD WHITE MALES.

IF YOU WANT TO STAY "DAD," I'D SUGGEST YOU ADOPT SOME KEY PLANKS TO YOUR PLATFORM.

SOME SPECIAL INTEREST GROUPS ARE IN FOR A SURPRISE.

OF THOSE POLLED, VIRTUALLY ALL FAVOR INCREASED ALLOWANCES AND THE COMMENCEMENT OF DRIVING LESSONS.

THERE'S A NEW GIRL IN OUR CLASS.

WELL! WHAT'S HER NAME?

WHO KNOWS?

IS SHE NICE?

WHO CARES? NOT ME!

DO YOU *LIKE* HER??

NO!

HERE COMES THAT NEW GIRL.

HEY SUSIE DERKINS, IS THAT YOUR FACE, OR IS A 'POSSUM STUCK IN YOUR COLLAR?

I HOPE YOU SUFFER A DEBILITATING BRAIN ANEURYSM, YOU FREAK!

SHE'S *CUTE*, ISN'T SHE??

GO AWAY.

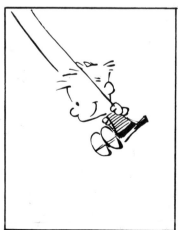

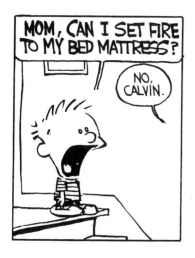

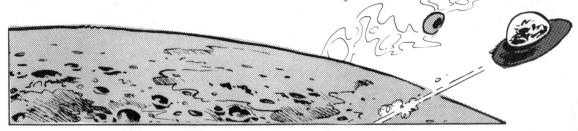

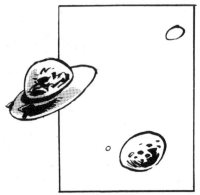

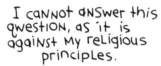

28

37

HI, DAD. IT'S ME, CALVIN!

HOW'S WORK GOING? ...UH HUH... PRETTY DAY OUT, ISN'T IT? ...YEP.....

ARE YOU BRINGING ME HOME ANY PRESENTS TONIGHT? ...NO? WELL, JUST THOUGHT I'D ASK...

LISTEN, I SUPPOSE YOU'RE WONDERING WHY I CALLED...

DAD, YOUR POLLS TOOK A BIG DIVE THIS WEEK.

YOUR "OVERALL DAD PERFORMANCE" RATING WAS ESPECIALLY LOW.

SEE? RIGHT ABOUT YESTERDAY YOUR POPULARITY WENT DOWN THE TUBES.

CALVIN, YOU DIDN'T GET DESSERT YESTERDAY BECAUSE YOU FLOODED THE HOUSE!!

I'D SUGGEST A NEW LINE OF WORK, "DAD"...

THE GIANT SLIMY OCTOPUS OOZES ACROSS THE BEACH.

HIS HIDEOUS PRESENCE TERRORIZES THE SLEEPY WATERFRONT COMMUNITY.

WITH A SUCKER-COVERED TENTACLE, HE GRABS AN UNSUSPECTING TOURIST.

A MUFFLED SCREAM LINGERS IN THE SALTY AIR!

DID YOU WANT SOMETHING, CALVIN?

ACK ICK IG

38

44

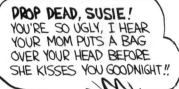

Hey, Calvin, it's gonna cost you 50 cents to be my friend today.

AND WHAT IF I DON'T *WANT* TO BE YOUR FRIEND TODAY?

Then the janitor scrapes you off the wall with a spatula.

HECK, WHAT'S A LITTLE EXTORTION AMONG FRIENDS?

I GOT THE NEW ALBUM BY SCRAMBLED DEBUTANTE.

ALL THEIR SONGS GLORIFY DEPRAVED VIOLENCE, MINDLESS SEX, AND THE DELIBERATE ABUSE OF DANGEROUS DRUGS.

YOUR MOM'S GOING TO GO INTO CONNIPTIONS WHEN SHE SEES *THIS* LYING AROUND.

WELL I SURE DIDN'T BUY IT FOR THE MUSIC...

MOM, WILL YOU DRIVE ME INTO TOWN?

WHY SHOULD I *DRIVE* YOU, CALVIN? IT'S A PERFECT DAY OUTSIDE!

WHAT DO YOU THINK PEOPLE HAVE *FEET* FOR?

TO WORK THE GAS PEDAL.

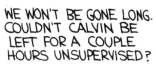

DO YOU LOVE ME, DAD?

OF COURSE I DO, CALVIN.

WOULD YOU STILL LOVE ME IF I DID SOMETHING BAD?

WELL OF COURSE ... I ... WOULD...

I MEAN SOMETHING REALLY *REALLY*..

CALVIN, WHAT DID YOU DO?!

WELL, DAD, YOUR POLLS ARE REAL HIGH THIS WEEK.

I'M GLAD TO HEAR THAT.

YEP, THOSE POLLED THINK YOU'RE DOING A FINE JOB AS DAD.

IN FACT, WITH A LITTLE PUSH TODAY, YOUR POLITICAL STOCK COULD REACH A RECORD HIGH.

NICE TRY. GO HELP YOUR MOM WITH THE DISHES.

OOH DAD! SUICIDE! OOH! OOH!

HERE COMES MOE, THE CLASS BULLY.

HE'S NOT SMART, BUT HE'S STREETWISE.

THAT MEANS HE KNOWS WHAT STREET HE LIVES ON.

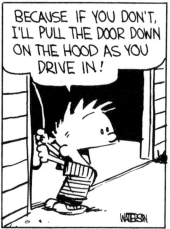

SOMEWHERE IN COMMUNIST RUSSIA I'LL BET THERE'S A LITTLE BOY WHO HAS NEVER KNOWN ANYTHING BUT **CENSORSHIP** AND **OPPRESSION**.

BUT MAYBE HE'S HEARD ABOUT **AMERICA**, AND HE DREAMS OF LIVING IN THIS LAND OF **FREEDOM** AND OPPORTUNITY!

SOMEDAY, I'D LIKE TO MEET THAT LITTLE BOY...

...AND TELL HIM THE AWFUL **TRUTH** ABOUT THIS PLACE.!!

CALVIN, BE QUIET AND EAT THE STUPID LIMA BEANS.

WHENEVER I TAKE MY BATH...

...I ALWAYS PUT MY DUCKY IN FIRST.

FOR COMPANIONSHIP?

TO TEST FOR SHARKS.

MY SECRET ANCIENT TREASURE MAP SAYS TO DIG HERE!

LOOK! A WALLET FULL OF MONEY! RIGHT WHERE YOU SAID!

IT'S DAD'S. I BURIED IT HERE LAST WEEK.

74

WHERE'S MY JACKET?

I'VE LOOKED EVERYWHERE! UNDER THE BED, OVER MY CHAIR...

...ON THE STAIRS, ON THE HALL FLOOR, IN THE KITCHEN... IT'S JUST NOT ANYWHERE!

OH, *HERE* IT IS! WHO PUT IT IN THE STUPID CLOSET?!?

HOCUS-POCUS, ABRACADABRA!

I COMMAND MY HOMEWORK TO DO ITSELF! **HOMEWORK, BE DONE!**

FLIP FLIP FLIP

RATS.

DO YOU EVER THINK ABOUT THE END OF THE WORLD AS WE KNOW IT?

YOU MEAN A NUCLEAR WAR?

I THINK MOM WAS REFERRING TO IF SHE EVER CATCHES ME LETTING THE AIR OUT OF THE CAR TIRES AGAIN.

79

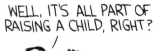

CALVIN, THE HUMAN INSECT, WALKS ACROSS THE DINNER TABLE.

WITH PROPORTIONAL INSECT STRENGTH, HE PLACES A GIANT PEA ON THE EDGE OF A SPOON.

HE THEN CLIMBS TO THE TOP OF THE OTHER END...

...AND WITH A TINY JUMP...

CALVIN, STOP THAT!

IN HIS MINUSCULE SIZE, IT TAKES CALVIN, THE HUMAN INSECT, TEN MINUTES TO WALK ACROSS A BOOK'S PAGE!

AT THE OTHER END, HE SLOWLY LIFTS THE GIGANTIC SHEET!

THEN IT'S ANOTHER TEN-MINUTE JOURNEY BACK, AS HE TURNS IT OVER!

GEE, THE KID'S BEEN QUIET FOR ALMOST TWENTY MINUTES.

HE'S DOING HIS HOMEWORK.

HERE'S A MOVIE WE SHOULD WATCH.

WHO'S IN IT?

IT SAYS, "JAPANESE CAST."

"TWO BIG RUBBERY MONSTERS SLUG IT OUT OVER MAJOR METROPOLITAN CENTERS IN A BATTLE FOR WORLD SUPREMACY."

DOESN'T THAT SOUND GREAT?

AND PEOPLE SAY THAT FOREIGN FILM IS INACCESSIBLE.

OH, ROSALYN, YOU'RE HERE! GOOD, COME IN!

WE REALLY APPRECIATE YOUR COMING ON SUCH SHORT NOTICE. WE'VE HAD A TERRIBLE TIME GETTING A BABY SITTER FOR TONIGHT.

HA HA, MAYBE LITTLE CALVIN HERE HAS GOTTEN HIMSELF A REPUTATION.

HA HA. YOU HAVE THE HALF UP FRONT?

YES, LET ME GET MY PURSE...

HI, BABY DOLL, IT'S ME. YEAH, I'M BABY SITTING THE KID DOWN THE STREET.

YEAH, THAT'S RIGHT, THE LITTLE MONSTER. ...HMM?... WELL SO FAR, NO PROBLEM.

HE HASN'T BEEN ANY TROUBLE. YOU JUST HAVE TO SHOW THESE KIDS WHO'S THE BOSS. ...MM HMM..

HOW MUCH LONGER TILL SHE LETS US OUT OF THE GARAGE?

SHE SAID 8 O'CLOCK, AND IT'S ALMOST 6:30 NOW...

THANKS AGAIN FOR BABY SITTING, ROSALYN.

CALVIN WAS NO TROUBLE AT ALL.

THAT'S GOOD. I'LL GET THE CAR AND DRIVE YOU HOME.

THERE YOU GO. GOOD NIGHT.

THANK YOU. GOOD NIGHT.

IS SHE GONE?

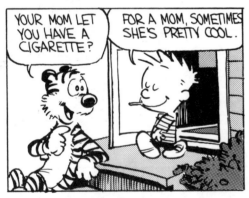

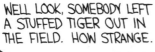

WELL LOOK, SOMEBODY LEFT A STUFFED TIGER OUT IN THE FIELD. HOW STRANGE.

LOOKS LIKE A DOG'S BEEN CHEWING ON YOU, FELLA.

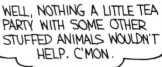

WELL, NOTHING A LITTLE TEA PARTY WITH SOME OTHER STUFFED ANIMALS WOULDN'T HELP. C'MON.

HOBBES! HOBBES! WHERE ARE YOU??

HELLO, CALVIN. WOULD YOU LIKE TO JOIN MY TEA PARTY?

HECK NO. I'M TRYING TO FIND MY BEST FRIEND, WHO'S BEEN KIDNAPPED BY A DOG. LEAVE ME ALONE.

WELL I THINK MR. CALVIN IS VERY RUDE, DON'T YOU, MR. TIGER? YES, I THINK SO TOO. MORE TEA, ANYONE?

HEY, I SHOULD TELL SUSIE TO KEEP HER EYES OPEN FOR HOBBES.

SUSIE, I... HOBBES!

YOU FOUND HOBBES! THANK YOU THANK YOU THANKYOUTHANKYOUTHANKY OUTHANKYOUTHANKYOUTHA

WELL! WASN'T MR. CALVIN A GENTLEMAN! I DO HOPE... HEY! WHO TOOK ALL THE COOKIES?!?

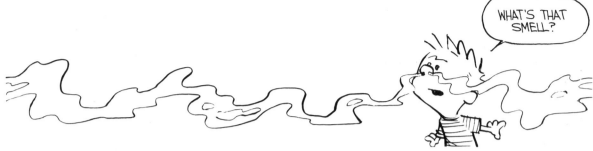

SUSIE, WANNA HEAR A SECRET?

SURE.

I THINK THE PRINCIPAL IS A SPACE ALIEN SPY.

HE'S TRYING TO CORRUPT OUR YOUNG INNOCENT MINDS SO WE'LL BE UNABLE TO RESIST WHEN HIS PEOPLE INVADE EARTH!

PROMISE NOT TO TELL ANYONE?

DON'T WORRY.

HOBBES, WHAT SHOULD I DO WHEN MOE COMES TO BEAT ME UP IN GYM CLASS?

WELL, YOU CAN ALWAYS DO WHAT WE TIGERS DO WHEN A RHINO CHARGES.

WHAT'S THAT?

WE SCRAMBLE LIKE MANIACS FOR THE NEAREST TREE.

THAT'S YOUR ADVICE?? TO SIT IN A TREE ALL DAY?!?

IT DOESN'T IMPRESS THE GIRLS, OF COURSE, BUT THERE'S NO SENSE IMPRESSING THEM AND THEN GETTING KILLED, MY DAD USED TO SAY...

HOBBES, I NEED YOUR HELP. THAT BULLY MOE KEEPS PUSHING ME AROUND.

...SO I WANT YOU TO COME TO SCHOOL AND EAT HIM, OK?

EAT HIM?

SURE! TIGERS EAT PEOPLE ALL THE TIME!

WHAT IF THE CAFETERIA LADIES WON'T LET ME USE THE OVEN?

IT'S TOO EARLY TO BE IN BED. IT'S HARDLY EVEN DARK OUT. WHY DO I HAVE TO BE IN BED? IT'S RIDICULOUS.

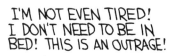

I'M NOT EVEN TIRED! I DON'T NEED TO BE IN BED! THIS IS AN OUTRAGE!

IT'S THE STUPIDEST THING I CAN IMAGINE! I THINK MOM AND DAD ARE JUST TRYING TO GET RID OF ME. I CAN'T SLEEP AT ALL. CAN YOU SLEEP, HOBBES?

NO!

OK, MOM, HOBBES AND I HAVE FORMED A LOBBY. WE WANT MORE PRIVILEGES!

MORE PRIVILEGES? LIKE WHAT? YOU'VE GOT IT MADE!

NO RESPONSIBILITIES, NO CARES, NO WORRIES! WHAT MORE COULD YOU POSSIBLY WANT?

WHY DIDN'T YOU TELL HER ABOUT THE CREDIT CARDS IN OUR NAMES?

YOU HEARD HER. SHE'S IN ONE OF HER MOODS.

I LOVE SATURDAYS!

EVERY SATURDAY I GET UP AT SIX AND EAT THREE BOWLS OF CRUNCHY SUGAR BOMBS.

THEN I WATCH CARTOONS TILL NOON, AND I'M INCOHERENT AND HYPERACTIVE THE REST OF THE DAY.

DOES IT WORK?

NO BROTHERS OR SISTERS **SO** FAR!

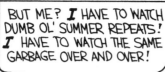

WHEN ARE WE GOING TO GET TO OUR VACATION SITE? I WANNA *BE* THERE!

CALVIN, IT'S AN EIGHT-HOUR DRIVE. WE'RE NOT EVEN OUT OF OUR STATE YET. IT'S GOING TO BE A WHILE. RELAX.

HOW MUCH LONGER *NOW*?

I TOLD YOU WE SHOULD HAVE FLOWN.

THERE'S A RESTAURANT COMING UP. WANT TO STOP?

ONLY IF THEY HAVE HAMBURGERS.

HAMBURGERS? THAT'S ALL WE'VE EATEN THIS WHOLE STUPID TRIP! HAMBURGERS, HAMBURGERS, HAMBURGERS!

I'M SICK OF HAMBURGERS! WE'RE EATING SOMETHING ELSE FOR ONCE!

TEN MILLION BOTTLES OF BEER ON THE WALL, TEN MILLION BOTTLES OF BEER...

OK! OK! HERE'S A HAMBURGER JOINT! *ARE YOU HAPPY?!*

I HAVE TO GO TO THE BATHROOM.

CALVIN, WE JUST PULLED OUT OF THE RESTAURANT. CAN'T YOU WAIT? THINK OF SOMETHING ELSE.

ALL I CAN THINK OF IS NIAGARA FALLS, AND THE HOOVER DAM, AND NOAH'S ARK, AND...

OOH BOY, NOW *I* HAVE TO GO!

NEXT YEAR I SWEAR I'LL JUST TAKE A VACATION BY MYSELF.

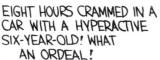

I DON'T *LIKE* FOOD COOKED OUT, DO YOU?

UGH. IT ALL TASTES THE SAME.

FLOWERS ARE PRETTY STUPID.

SEE, IT'S A BRIGHT, SUNNY DAY OUT, RIGHT?

WELL, WITH THIS WATERING CAN, I CAN MAKE THEM THINK IT'S RAINING.

IT'S FUN TO MESS WITH THEIR MINDS.

THE EXPERIMENT HAS GONE HORRIBLY WRONG! CALVIN HAS MUTATED INTO A GIANT FLY!

HE ZIPS ABOUT IN PARASITIC HUNGER, SEARCHING FOR DECAYING FLESH!

AN UNBEARABLE STENCH FILLS THE AIR. THE HIDEOUS BUG ZEROES IN.

MMM! THIS MAKES ME HUNGRY!

DON'T BE GROSS. JUST TAKE OUT THE GARBAGE LIKE I ASKED YOU, WILL YOU PLEASE?

IT'S ANOTHER NEW MORNING FOR MR. MONROE. HE GLANCES AT THE NEWSPAPER HEADLINES OVER A CUP OF COFFEE, AND GETS IN HIS RED SPORTS CAR TO GO TO WORK.

LITTLE DOES HE REALIZE IT'S HIS LAST DAY ON THE FACE OF THE EARTH!

CALVIN DRINKS THE MAGIC ELIXIR AND BEGINS AN INCREDIBLE TRANSFORMATION!

INSTANTLY HE GROWS! BIGGER AND BIGGER! HIGHER AND HIGHER!

HE IS NOW OVER 300 FEET TALL! THE FORMULA IS A SUCCESS!

CALVIN, THE MIGHTY GIANT, GOES ON A TERRIBLE RAMPAGE, STRIKING FEAR INTO THE HEARTS OF THE POPULACE!

NOTHING CAN STOP HIM! IT'S PANIC IN THE STREETS! A TOWN LIES IN RUINS!

NO, I WON'T BUY YOU ANY MORE TOY CARS. I SAW YOU! YOU DELIBERATELY STOMPED ON THOSE!

WATTERSON

115

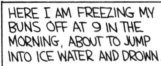

LOOK AT THAT THING IN THE DIRT! IT MUST BE A FOSSIL!

I WONDER WHAT PECULIAR ANIMAL *THIS* WAS.

BUT IT'S NOT A BONE. IT MUST BE SOME PRIMITIVE HUNTING WEAPON OR EATING UTENSIL FOR CAVE MEN.

MAYBE IT HAD SOME RELIGIOUS FUNCTION.

THIS EXPLAINS WHY YOUR CLOTHES STAY ON THE FLOOR.

MAKING A SIGN?

I'M DECLARING THE CREEK BACK IN THE WOODS "CALVIN'S CREEK."

WHEN YOU DISCOVER SOMETHING, YOU'RE ALLOWED TO NAME IT AND PUT UP A SIGN.

Calvins CrEEK

BUT SUPPOSE YOU DIDN'T DISCOVER THAT CREEK.

OF COURSE I DID! NOBODY *ELSE* HAS A SIGN THERE, RIGHT?

Hobs crk

CAN HOBBES AND I GO PLAY IN THE RAIN, MOM?

NO.

WHY NOT?

YOU'LL GET SOAKED.

WHAT'S WRONG WITH THAT?

YOU COULD CATCH PNEUMONIA, RUN UP A TERRIBLE HOSPITAL BILL, LINGER A FEW MONTHS, AND DIE.

I ALWAYS FORGET. IF YOU ASK A MOM, YOU GET A WORST-CASE SCENARIO.

I HAD NO IDEA THESE LITTLE SHOWERS WERE SO *DANGEROUS*.

HERE COMES SUSIE.

HA! WON'T SHE BE HORRIFIED TO SEE HOW OUR FACES HAVE TRAGICALLY FROZEN!

HI, SUSIE.

HI, CALVIN.

WHAT DID YOU DO, GET YOUR HEAD STUCK IN THE BLENDER? IT'S AN IMPROVEMENT.

ARE THE COALS HOT?

YES, THEY'RE VERY HOT. I'M JUST ABOUT TO PUT ON THE HAMBURGERS.

BEFORE YOU DO, COULD YOU TOSS IN THE CAN OF LIGHTER FLUID AND MAKE A GIANT FIREBALL?

I'VE GOT THE MOST BORING DAD IN THE WORLD.

WITH THESE SNORKELS, WE CAN STAY UNDER WATER INDEFINITELY.

JUST THINK OF ALL THE FISH WE'LL BE ABLE TO SEE!

WE CAN COLLECT SHELLS!

LET'S GO!

WELL SO FAR, THIS HAS BEEN A MAJOR DISAPPOINTMENT.

Finis